C000200760

Jam tarts

Written by Gill Munton

Speed Sounds

Consonants *Ask children to say the sounds.*

f	l	m	n	r	s	v	z	sh	**th**	ng
ff	ll	mm	nn	rr	ss	ve	zz			nk
	le		kn		se		**se**			
					ce		s			

b	c	d	g	h	j	p	qu	t	w	x	y	**ch**
bb	k	dd	gg		g	pp		tt	wh			tch
	ck				**ge**							

Each box contains one sound but sometimes more than one grapheme.
*Focus graphemes for this story are **circled**.*

Vowels *Ask children to say the sounds in and out of order.*

a	e ea	i	o	u	ay	ee y	igh	ow
at	hen	in	on	up	day	see	high	blow

oo	oo	ar	or oor ore	air	ir	ou	oy
zoo	look	car	for	fair	whirl	shout	boy

Story Green Words

Ask children to read the words first in Fred Talk and then say the word.

Mark   car   park   list   cheese   jar   large

jam   tart

Ask children to say the syllables and then read the whole word.

coff|ee   sham|poo   pack|et

Ask children to read the root first and then the whole word with the suffix.

egg → eggs   plum → plums   nut → nuts

mushroom → mushrooms

Vocabulary Check

Discuss the meaning (as used in the non-fiction text) after the children have read the word.

	definition
needed	*had to get*
plums	*soft, juicy fruit*
mushrooms	*little umbrella-shaped things that you eat*

Red Words

of	we	to	was
she	some	the	he
want	what	no	said
call	go	all	be

Mum needed lots of things from the shop.

I got in the car with Mum and Mark.

We went to the shop. It was not far away.
Mum parked in the car park.

Mum had a long list.

Shopping list

coffee

pop

eggs

cheese

plums

nuts

mushrooms

shampoo

Mum got a big jar of coffee and six cans of pop.

She got a box of large eggs and a packet of cheese.

She got a box of plums and a packet of nuts.

She got a box of mushrooms and some shampoo. But Mark got ...

... six jam tarts!

Questions to talk about

Ask children to TTYP for each question using 'Fastest finger' (FF) or 'Have a think' (HaT).

p.9 (FF) Where are they going?

p.10 (FF) Where did Mum park?

p.11 (FF) What is at the top of Mum's shopping list?

p.12 (FF) What was the coffee in?

p.13 (FF) How big were the eggs?

p.16 (HaT) Do you think Mum was cross with Mark? Why or why not?

Questions to read and answer

(Children complete without your help.)

1. Mum got a big jar of **pop** / **coffee** / **nuts**.

2. Mum got **three** / **six** / **ten** cans of pop.

3. Mum got a box of **cheese** / **shampoo** / **mushrooms**.

4. Mark got **jam tarts** / **nuts** / **plums**.

5. Mark got **six** / **ten** / **three** jam tarts.